KEYHOLE KATE

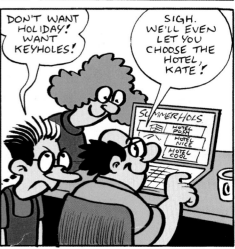

LEW STRINGER

the JOCKS and the GEORDIES

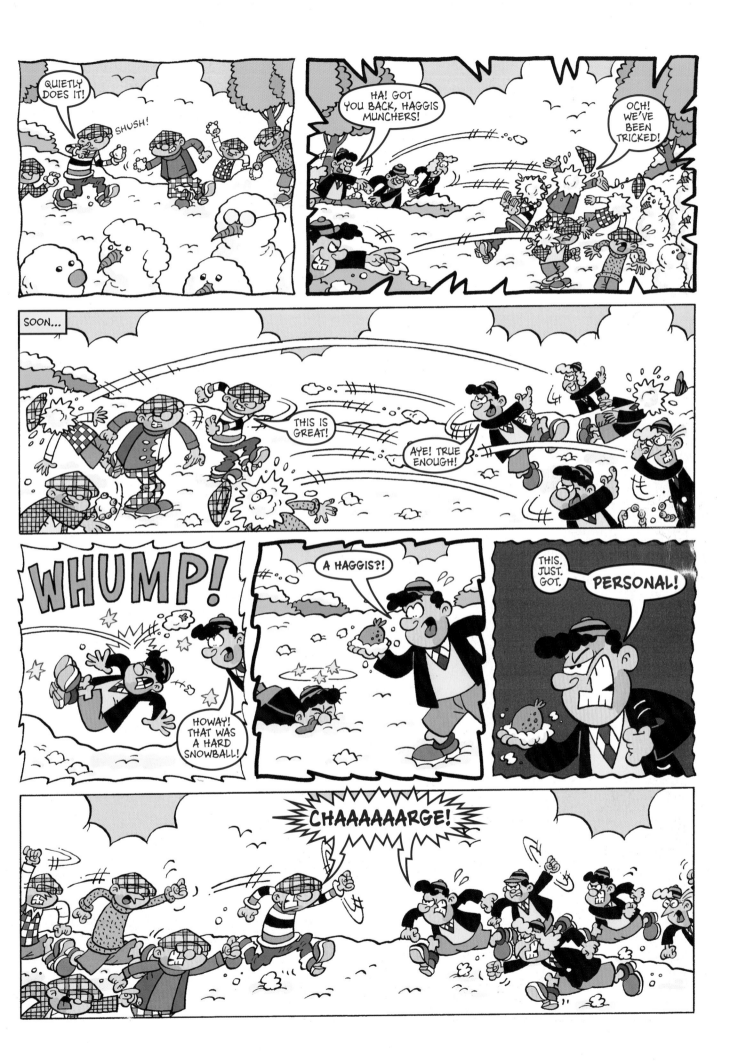

BULLY BEEF and CHIPS

IT SAYS HERE YOU HAVE TWO CHOICES - FIGHT OR FLIGHT.

HOW TO BEAT BULLIES

SO WHICH ONE YOU GONNA CHOOSE?

GLURK! B-B-BEEFY!

NO BRAINER! FIGHT, OF COURSE!

HAW-HAW! WRONG CHOICE, BOOKWORM!

THUMP

I'D CHOOSE FLIGHT NEXT TIME IF I WERE YOU! GUFFAW!

URRGH!

DANDYTOWN AIRFIELD

I THINK I WILL TAKE BEEFY'S ADVICE!

WOULD YOU TAKE ME UP FOR A SPIN, UNCLE MAC?

MY PLEASURE, CHIPS. JUMP IN.

CHORTLE! SOPPY-BOY WON'T BOTHER ME AGAIN TODAY.

I ALWAYS WAS THE HIGH-FLYER, PAL!

ZOOOM!

W-W-WHAT?!

OOOYAH-GLUBB!

FLIGHT IS DEFINITELY THE BETTER OPTION. CHUCKLE!

BLEHH!

KORKY THE CAT

FIDDLE O'DIDDLE

HEY, MULDOON! HAVE YOU BOUGHT ME A CHRISTMAS PRESENT YET?

I HAVE NOT!

I'VE NO MONEY FOR BUYING YOU PRESENTS!

THAT'S EASILY SOLVED. YOU CAN RAISE SOME MONEY CAROL SINGING!

Fiddle's Christmas Carols

YOU'LL NEED TO WARM UP YOUR VOCAL CORDS FIRST.

HO-HO! MULDOON IS THE BIGGEST IDIOT THERE EVER WAS!

EXTRA HOT MINTS

VINDALOO SOUP

HERE'S A GOOD SPOT.

NICK BRENNAN

GOOD KING WENCESLAS LOOKED DOWN, AT HIS PLATE WITH PEAS ON...

YOU HAVE THE VOICE OF AN ANGEL, MULDOON!

COTTON WOOL

...IT WAS SITTING ON HIS LEGS, WHICH HE KEPT HIS KNEES ON.

IT'S THAT STRAY CAT AGAIN!

THE SMASHER!

BERYL The PERIL

BORED, BORED, BORED, BO-O-ORED!

STILL TIME TO WAIT, SO I'LL HAVE A HUNT IN THE ATTIC - SEE IF THERE'S ANY OLD PHOTOS OF DAD TO LAUGH AT.

OH, WOW! EVEN BETTER!

LOOKY HERE! TREASURE! LET THE FUN BEGIN!

BERYL'S SEARCH FOR THE BIG GAME WAS HALTED AS A HUGE SAVAGE BEAST BLOCKED HER PATH THROUGH THE JUNGLE...

...AND ALL BERYL HAD WAS HER TRUSTY MOP. WHICH WASN'T MUCH USE IN THE JUNGLE.

THE MONSTROUS PREDATOR HAD ONLY ONE THOUGHT IN HIS HEAD...

...TO ATTACK, ATTACK, ATTACK!

LICK LICK LICK

GERROFF! HEH!

BERYL AND HER FAITHFUL COMPANION SET FORTH INTO THE JUNGLE TO SEARCH FOR THE BIG GAME. WE'LL TAKE THE BUS.

BIG CAT! I NEED TO SHOOT IT...

WHAT?! WE CAN'T HAVE THAT IN THE DANDY ANNUAL! - ED

...TO SHOW DAD WHEN I GET HOME.

CLICK!

OH! - ED

HE'S A SUCKER FOR A CUTE CAT PIC!

BUT...

WHUMP!

CAREFUL, YOUNG LADY - YOU'LL CAUSE YOURSELF AN INJURY!

SORRY, OFFICER. WON'T HAPPEN AGAIN.

SEE THAT IT DOESN'T!

I WILL! TEE-HEE!

agent dog 2 zero

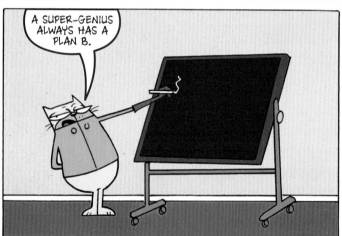

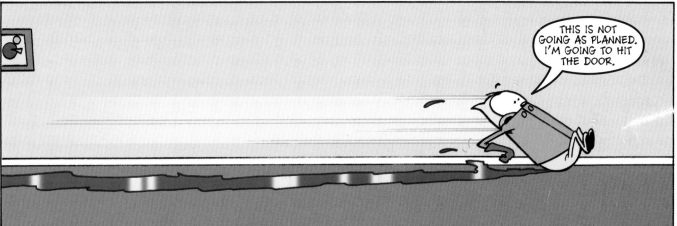

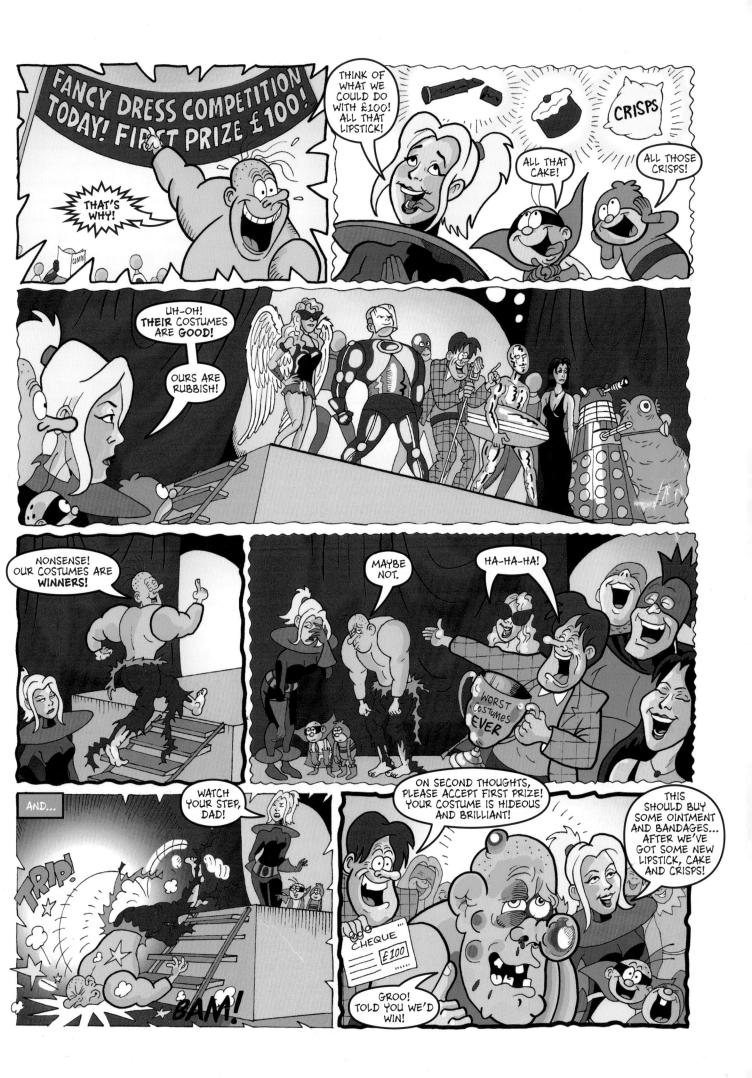

LEW STRINGER

WHAT? THAT OLD SKINFLINT?

HE MUST BE FULL OF CHRISTMAS SPIRIT.

SO WHO'S GETTING WHAT?

I WANT THE CAMERA!

I WANT THE TELLY!

THE BIKE FOR ME!

THAT TELLY'S MINE!

NO, MINE!

I SAW IT FIRST!

MY BIKE!

OOF! MY TELLY!

OUCH! MY PHONE!

THUP!

WHAT ARE YOU FIGHTING ABOUT?

YOUR LIST.

THERE'S NO NEED TO FIGHT...

...IF YOU ALL CHIP IN YOU CAN BUY ME THOSE THINGS BETWEEN YOU.

WE'RE SUPPOSED TO BUY YOU PRESENTS?!

THE WAY YOU TREAT US?

THE WAGES YOU PAY?

ULP!

SKINFLINT!

CHEAPSKATE!

SCROOGE!

LOOKS LIKE IT'LL BE PANTS AGAIN THIS YEAR!

DESPERATE DAN

NOW WE'VE TRANSFORMED THE TRAIN INTO A MECHANICAL MAN, WE SHOULD CALL IT **TRAINSFORMER!**

PAW! I WANNA CALL HIM OPTIMUS TRAIN!

THE CLANTON'S PLACE

THEY'RE BOTH STUPID NAMES! WE'RE GONNA CALL HIM TRAIN MAN! AND HE'S GONNA HELP US STEAL A WHOLE LOAD OF MONEY!

LATER...

DAN! THE CLANTONS ARE HEADING FOR TOWN IN A GIANT MECHANICAL MAN MADE OUT OF TRAINS!

THEY'VE GONE OFF THE RAILS AGAIN!

PRICES

CREAM SODA

I'LL DEAL WITH THIS! I AM THE SHERIFF, AFTER ALL!

MY WORD!

I QUIT! YOU DEAL WITH IT!

SURE!

CHOO! CHOO!

WHEN I PULL THIS, TRAIN MAN TALKS!

AND HE MAKES MORE SENSE THAN YOU!

POSTMAN PRAT

LEW STRINGER.

CORPORAL CLOTT

IT'S INSPECTION TIME...

STAND BY YOUR BEDS!

COLONEL GRUMBLY HAS AN EYE FOR DETAIL...

GOOD, TIGHT CORNERS, SOLDIER.

CLOTT! THAT DUVET IS NOT REGULATION!

AND IS THAT FOX EATING SOUP?

I TRIED TO TELL MR FOXERSON NOT TO, BUT HE GETS GRUMPY WHEN HE'S HUNGRY.

GRRR!!!

NO, MR FOXERSON! HE DOESN'T WANT YOUR SOUP!

ARRRGH!

CLOTT IS PUT ON TIDYING DUTY AS PUNISHMENT...

THIS IS OUR MESSIEST SHELL SHED. TIDY IT UP!

I'M ON IT NOW, YOUR EMINENCE!

WATCH OUT, CLOTT!

TRIP!

ROLL!

CLONK!

PHEW! I THOUGHT IT WAS ABOUT TO EXPLODE!

WHO AM I?

THAT KNOCK ON YOUR NOGGIN MUST HAVE MADE YOU LOSE YOUR MEMORY.

YOU'RE A BRILLIANT SOLDIER! THE BEST IN THE COUNTRY!

SIR! YES, SIR!

BULLY BEEF and CHIPS

BLINKY

agent dog 2 zero

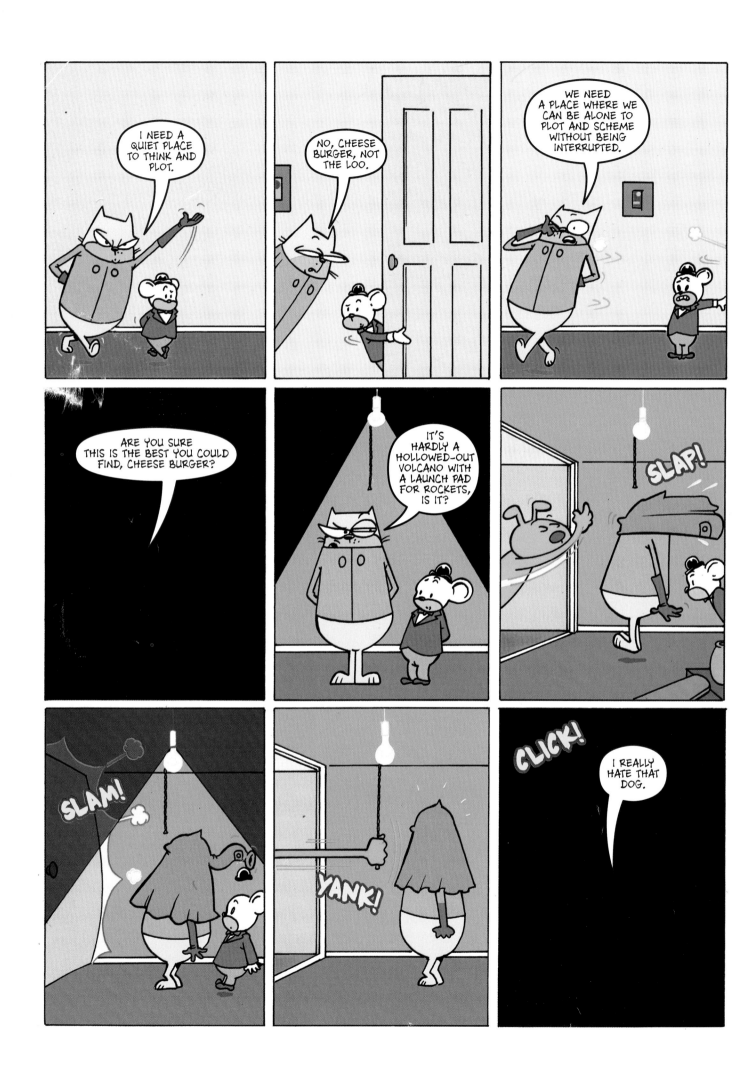

I WANT AN UNDERGROUND LAIR!

WITH LASERS... AND A TOASTIE MAKER.

AND BEST OF ALL, MY ARCH ENEMY WILL DO THE WORK FOR ME!

BONES HERE.

JUICY BONES.

BURIED BONES.

MORE BONES.

BONES! BONES!! BONES!!!

BONES HERE!

BONES?

BONES UNDER MASTER'S LOVELY GRASS?

MASTER LOVES HIS LAWN, BUT I LOVE BONES! I MUSTN'T! I WON'T DIG... NO, NO, NO...

...BUT I WILL!

AGENT DOG 2 ZERO HAS FALLEN INTO MY CUNNING TRAP. HE IS DIGGING UP MASTER'S PRIZE LAWN, AND WHILE MASTER IS MIFFED AT HIM – I SHALL BUILD MY UNDERGROUND BASE!

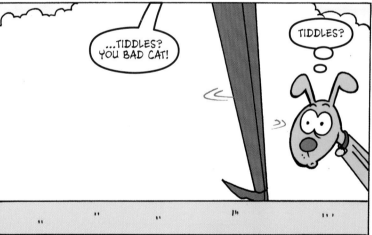

KORKY THE CAT

THE SMASHER!

BERYL The PERIL

TODAY IS 'TAKE YOUR DAUGHTER TO WORK DAY'. NO, IT REALLY IS THIS TIME...

I'M DEAD EXCITED, DAD!

HEH! I CAN SEE THAT.

YOU GO AND WAIT IN THE CAR - I'LL JUST GRAB MY BRIEFCASE.

WILL DO, POPS!

I'M GLAD THAT YOU'RE KEEN, BUT YOU'RE NOT DRIVING!

RATS!

I CAN'T WAIT TO SEE YOU IN ACTION, DAD. HOW YOU OPERATE... MEET YOUR WORKMATES. JUST ONE QUESTION...

FIRE AWAY!

...WHAT IS IT THAT YOU ACTUALLY DO?

WHAT? YOU DON'T KNOW?

SIGH!

MORNING SMITHERS!

MORNING, SIR!

WOW! HE'S IMPORTANT!

IT'S A LITTLE COMPLICATED...

I'M LISTENING.

...BUT BASICALLY...

HELP! HELP! I'M BEING ATTACKED BY CREATURES FROM OUTER SPACE! HELP!

WHASSAT?!

BERYL, YOU HAVE TO PROMISE NEVER TO REVEAL WHAT'S ABOUT TO HAPPEN!

I PROMISE! WHAT'S GOING ON, DAD?

I'M **SUPERDAD!** DEFENDER OF JUSTICE, RIGHTER OF WRONGS!

RRRI-I-I-I-I-I-PP!

PING! PING! PING!

WH-WHAT?! GERRAWAY!

STAY RIGHT THERE, BERYL — I'LL BE BACK JUST AS SOON AS I'VE SAVED THE WORLD FROM THIS ALIEN INVASION.

DAD! WE'RE ON THE 27TH FLOOR!

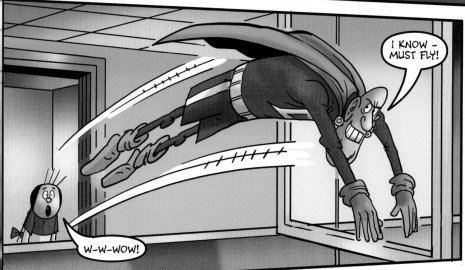

I KNOW — MUST FLY!

W-W-WOW!

M-MY DAD... IS A SUPERHERO!

TSIDE...

D SHE L FOR IT?

ACE WINDOW CLEANERS

BRIGHTY

HOOK, LINE AND SINKER — THE RADIO LINK TO THE ELEVATOR WORKED A TREAT! I'LL LET HER IN ON THE JOKE SHORTLY...

MY DAD'S A SUPERHERO! DON'T TELL ANYONE.

...JUST LET HER ENJOY THE MOMENT WHILE I CLEAN A FEW PANELS.

DONE IT!

I THINK YOU'RE FORGETTING SOMETHING, DAN. THERE'S A FEW OTHER THINGS FOR YOU TO TAKE CARE OF.

BYE!

OH YEAH! THE STAGECOACH!

AUNT AGGIE!

AND SAVING THE BEST TILL LAST... THE COW PIE!

COW PIE

THE BEST TILL LAST?

WITHOUT ME THERE ARE NO COW PIES, YA BIG GALOOT!

OUCH! I PREFERRED THE VIOLENT WEATHER!

CORPORAL CLOTT

INSTEAD OF PEELING POTATOES, CORPORAL CLOTT HAS CARVED ONE TO LOOK LIKE COLONEL GRUMBLY...

I'M MR GRUMBLY AND I'M CROSS ALL THE TIME!

CLOTT! THAT DOESN'T LOOK LIKE PEELING POTATOES TO ME!

ARRGH! IT SOUNDS JUST LIKE HIM!

GET OUTSIDE, AT ONCE!

SLAP!

YES, YOUR MAJESTY!

OUTSIDE...

A NEW TANK? WHERE DO I SIT?

I'M GLAD YOU ASKED. YOU SIT...

...HERE! PEELING POTATOES! AND THAT'S ALL.

DO NOT TOUCH MY NEW TANK! IT'S A DRONE. UNDERSTAND?

TOTALLY, YOUR LORDSHIP. I UNDERSTAND EVERYTHING!

REALLY?!

I DON'T HAVE A CLUE WHAT YOU'RE TALKING ABOUT!

IT'S A DRONE TANK, DRIVEN BY REMOTE CONTROL.

LIKE A TOY?!

IF BY 'TOY' YOU MEAN SOMETHING WHICH WILL GET YOU SHOT OUT OF A CANNON IF YOU TOUCH IT, THEN YES.

THAT'S NOT WHAT I MEANT AT ALL!

PEEL, BOIL AND MASH THOSE SPUDS!

I WONDER IF THE ONE THING I REMEMBER FROM SCHOOL CAN HELP ME HERE?

WAVES RUB STONES AGAINST EACH OTHER UNDERWATER, MAKING THEM SMOOTH AND ROUND WHEN THEY WASH ASHORE.

PINKY'S CRACKPOT CIRCUS

WE NEVER GET A HOLIDAY!

BUT WORKING IN THE CIRCUS IS FUN!

IT IS FOR YOU!

YOU JUST BOSS US ABOUT!

PAY US NOTHING!

AND KEEP ALL THE MONEY!

SO WE'RE ALL OFF ON OUR HOLS!

BUT WE'VE GOT A SHOW TONIGHT!

WHO WILL ENTERTAIN THE AUDIENCE?

YOU!

HMPH! WHO NEEDS THEM ANYWAY?

FOR I, PINKERTON GUSSET, WILL PUT ON THE **GREATEST SHOW ON EARTH...**

...SINGLE-HANDED!

THAT NIGHT...

FIRST... THE TIGHTROPE!

OO-ER... IT'S QUITE HIGH.

BOOO!

RUBBISH!

WOBBLE!

NICK BRENNAN

I GET A POUND EVERY TIME I WALK MRS MORRISON'S DOG.

CHARITY SHOP

SNIGGER! I KNOW HOW TO MAKE CHIPS BARKING MAD!

DRESSING UP CLOTHES

WANTID DOGWALKA

THAT'S BULLY BEEF'S GRAN'S HOUSE!

AWESOME! MORE WORK FOR ME!

GRRRR!

GLURK! THE DOG SOUNDS BIG... AND F-F-FIERCE!

URRRRGHHH!

GNASH! RIP! SHAKE!

WHIMPER!

IT'S A DOG-EAT-DOG WORLD, MY FRIEND! CHORTLE!

BEEFY'S GONE TOO FUR THIS TIME, BUT I'VE GOT A PLAN. I NEED TO DISTRACT HIM FOR JUST A MOMENT.

DROP!

LOOK, ALF! A MASSIVE STRAY.

DOG WARDEN

YAY! A DROPPED QUID. TODAY GETS BETTER AND BETTER!

GOT HIM!

CHEER UP, BEEFY! YOU'VE STILL GOT YOUR POUND - THE DOG POUND! CHUCKLE!

SNARL!

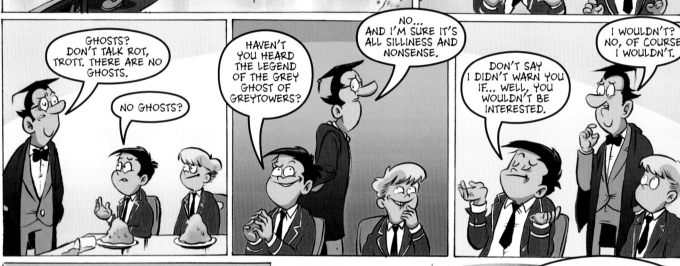

WHAT'S THE WANGLE, WINKER?

JUST WAIT... HELLO? IS THAT THE BRITAIN'S SPOOKIEST PLACES TV SHOW? I WAS WONDERING IF YOU WERE INTERESTED IN A HAUNTED SCHOOL?

SOON...

WE'RE HERE TO INVESTIGATE YOUR GREYTOWERS' GHOST.

I'VE NEVER HEARD ANYTHING SO SILLY. GO AWAY AT ONCE.

WE'LL PAY, OF COURSE.

ON THE OTHER HAND, DO COME IN AND WE'LL DO EVERYTHING WE CAN TO HELP YOU AND YOUR LOVELY MONEY.

WON'T THEY BE DISAPPOINTED WHEN THEY DON'T FIND ANY SIGN OF A GHOST?

DON'T WORRY, TROTTY. I HAVE ALL THE INFO I NEED IN HERE.

GHOSTS MAKE AWFUL NOISES - AND JENKINSON HERE HAD THE HADDOCK AND CABBAGE PIE FOR LUNCH.

GROAN! OOOOOOH!

SNIGGER!

OOOOOOH!

CAN YOU HEAR THAT POOR SOUL IN TORMENT?

YES, AND I WISH I COULDN'T.

IT SAYS HERE THAT GHOSTS PRODUCE A TERRIBLE SMELL.

THE BUMPER BOOK OF GHOSTS

TOMKINS?

TOMKINS!

TOMKINS' CHEESY FEET ARE LEGENDARY.

THEY'RE ENOUGH TO RAISE A GHOST!

HEY!

POSTMAN PRAT

POSTMAN PRAT IS DELIVERING PARCELS WHEN...

I DON'T REMEMBER THIS CRYING HOUSE ON MY ROUTE!

BOO HOO!

IT'S NOT THE HOUSE CRYING! WHAT'S UP, COWBOY?

I RUINED MY TOWN'S GALA! I'VE ALWAYS LIKED DANDYTOWN BUT CACTUSVILLE IS MY HOME!

HELP ME DELIVER MY PARCELS AND WE'LL FIGURE OUT WHAT TO DO!

SNIFF OKAY.

... SO YOU DESTROYED EVERYTHING?

YUP! HOW DO YOU DELIVER A FRIDGE?

EVERYTHING IS ALWAYS DELIVERED THROUGH THE LETTERBOX!

IT WON'T FIT.

EVERYTHING IS ALWAYS DELIVERED THROUGH THE LETTERBOX!

OKAY! OKAY!

DID THE TOWNSFOLK KNOW IT WAS JUST A MISTAKE?

YUP, BUT I'VE MADE A COUPLE OF MISTAKES IN THE PAST...

...ACCIDENTALLY DESTROYED THE TRAIN STATION, TOWN HALL, AND LIBRARY... AND THE SWEET SHOP... AND CATTLE MARKET, SALOON, THE...

PUSH!

OKAY, I GET THE IDEA! THE ONLY WAY THEY'LL LET YOU BACK IS IF YOU GIVE THEM THEIR GALA RIDES BACK!

BUT HOW? IT'S TOMORROW AND IT TOOK ME WEEKS TO BUILD!

YOU NEED HELP! PEOPLE IN DANDYTOWN ARE HELPFUL! I'LL GO 'ROUND TOWN AND DELIVER INVITATIONS TO EVERYONE TO HELP YOU OUT!

THANK YOU, POSTMAN PRAT!

AT THE ZOO...

COOKIE! I'M PRETTY SURE **ELEPHANTS** DON'T LAY EGGS!

YEAH THEY DO! LOOK! IT'S LAYING AN EGG NOW!

ARRGGH! THAT'S NOT AN EGG!

THE OSTRICH IS OUR BEST BET. IT'S PRETTY MUCH A GIANT CHICKEN AND IT'S PERFECTLY SAFE TO BE NEAR ONE.

ACTUALLY, A KICK FROM AN OSTRICH CAN SHATTER BONES!

OKAY, GOOD TO KNOW.

ARGH! IT'S GOT ME!

THE OSTRICH PULLS COOKIE IN AND SITS ON HER...

WHAT'S IT DOING?

I THINK IT'S TRYING TO HATCH COOKIE!

WHAT IF SHE **DOES** HATCH? WHAT IF SHE CRACKS AND A SLIGHTLY SMALLER COOKIE COMES OUT, LIKE ONE OF THOSE RUSSIAN DOLLS? I DON'T WANT TO SEE THAT!

WE NEED A DISTRACTION... I'VE GOT MY SOCK, BUT I NEED A CONE-SHAPED PARTY HAT!

HOW FORTUITOUS!

SO...

COO-EE! HEY, BABY! WHAT'S UP? I'M NOT SMALL, I'M FAR AWAY!

THAT DOESN'T LOOK LIKE AN OSTRICH! IT LOOKS LIKE A SOCK WITH A PARTY HAT ON IT!

IT'S WORKED! COOKIE'S ESCAPING. LET'S SCARPER!

CAN YOU BAKE A CAKE WITHOUT EGGS?

HEY, LOOK! THEY SELL OSTRICH EGGS IN THE GIFT SHOP!

GIFT SHOP

ZOO

SPECIAL OFFER! OSTRICH EGGS!

KEYHOLE KATE

KATE IS TURNING OVER A NEW LEAF...

THAT'S IT! I'M STOPPING PEEKING THROUGH KEYHOLES! IT'S A BAD HABIT!

BUT...

UH-OH!

SPECIAL INTERESTING JUICY SECRET INSIDE! ←

MAYBE ONE LAST PEEK!

GRAB!

WHAT THE--?

KATE IS PULLED THROUGH THE KEYHOLE!

SHOOP!

KEYHOLE KATE! WE ARE THE ANCIENT ORDER OF NOSEY PARKERS! WORD OF YOUR PEEKING POWERS HAS REACHED US!

BECAUSE CHRIS'S MUM GETS HIM THE DANDY ANNUAL EVERY YEAR!

YEAH, IT'S LIKE A THING WE DO! IT'S NICE BECAUSE I READ IT WITH MY KIDS NOW!

OKAY, WE'RE GETTING OFF TRACK! WE WISH TO BESTOW UPON YOU THE MAGIC DOOR KNOB! SIMPLY PLACE IT ON A WALL AND A DOOR WILL APPEAR AROUND IT!

NICE! I LIKE IT!

WITH THIS, YOU CAN CONTINUE OUR EVIL WORK!

EVIL?

YES, I SAID WE WERE AN EVIL ORDER AT THE START!

YOU SAID WE WERE AN ANCIENT ORDER, WHICH I THOUGHT WAS WEIRD BECAUSE WE ONLY GOT TOGETHER IN MARCH!

I'M NOT DOING EVIL!

OKAY, GIVE US THE MAGIC DOOR THING BACK, THEN!

KATE QUICKLY PUTS THE DOOR KNOB ON THE WALL, AND WHEN THE DOOR APPEARS SHE ESCAPES THROUGH IT!

STOP!

SEE? NOW WHAT'S THAT ABOUT? SHE SAYS SHE'S NOT EVIL, THEN PINCHES OUR MAGIC DOOR HANDLE!

KIDS TODAY!

TO BE CONTINUED...

THE JOCKS and THE GEORDIES

POSTMAN PRAT CONTINUES HIS DELIVERIES...

INSIDE THE GEORDIES' CLUB HOUSE...

HOWAY AND THAT, MAN. WE'VE GOT AN INVITATION TO MAK RIDES FOR THE CACTUSVILLE GALA!

MAK RIDES? WE'RE NOT MACKEMS, MAN!

PEOPLE TALK FUNNY UP NORTH! - ED

HANG ON! THIS INVITE WAS FOR THE JOCKS AND THAT!

MEANWHILE, INSIDE THE JOCKS' CLUB HOUSE...

THIS INVITE WAS FOR THE GEORDIES, THE NOO!

THE GEORDIES GOT AN INVITE, BUT WE DIDN'T?!

SO, THE GEORDIES THINK THE JOCKS WERE INVITED AND THEY WEREN'T, AND THE JOCKS THINK THE GEORDIES WERE INVITED AND THEY WEREN'T?

THIS IS WHERE THINGS CAN GET A BIT CONFUSING....

WE'LL MAKE A MASSIVE JOCK AND HIDE INSIDE TO CRASH THE PARTY, AND THAT!

LIKE THE TROJAN HORSE FROM GREEK MYTH, AND THAT!

WE'LL MAKE A PROPER MASSIVE GEORDIE AND HIDE INSIDE TO CRASH THE PARTY THE NOO!

LIKE THE TROJAN HORSE FROM GREEK MYTH!

EITHER SIDE OF HADRIAN'S WALL, THE JOCKS AND THE GEORDIES HAVE BUILT GIANT VERSIONS OF EACH OTHER...

INSIDE THE GIANT JOCK...

HANG ON! THAT'S NOT THE ANGEL OF THE NORTH, LIKE!

IT ALL KICKS OFF...

BIFF!

BOP!

THE TROJAN GEORDIE STUMBLES BACK AGAINST EDINBURGH CASTLE...

HOOTS, MON!

THE TROJAN JOCK FALLS BACK AGAINST THE TYNE BRIDGE...

WATCH YA DIVVENT SCRATCH IT, MAN!

BIFF!

UP NORTH, THINGS ARE A LOT CLOSER THAN THEY LOOK ON THE MAP! - ED

THE TROJAN JOCK AND GEORDIE EVENTUALLY FALL APART...

IT'S GOOSED, MAN! WE CANNAE GO TO THE PARTY NOO! YA KEN?

WHAT DOES THAT EVEN MEAN? LEARN TO TALK PROPER, LIKE!

I GIVE UP! - ED

THE JOCKS AND GEORDIES DISCOVER THAT IT IS ALL A MIX UP CAUSED BY POSTMAN PRAT...

OCH, AYE!

WHY, AYE!

SO, THEY CLUB TOGETHER TO BUILD ONE GIANT TROJAN HELTER SKELTER...

HAMMER!
SAW!
BANG!

BANG!
BUILD!
HAMMER!
SAW!

A HEART-WARMING MOMENT OF PEACE...

DANDYTOWN TRAIN STATION

HAPPY 80TH GALA CACTUSVILLE!

TRAIN TO CACTUSVILLE

...WHICH MIGHT LAST TILL THE END OF THE DAY. IF WE'RE LUCKY.

BULLY BEEF and CHIPS

CLACK!

THAT SOUNDS LIKE AN INVITATION TO MAKE AN ATTRACTION FOR CACTUSVILLE'S 80TH GALA!

DANDY

I WAS RIGHT! IT IS!

US CATS HAVE VERY GOOD HEARING!

IN THE LOFT...

I'LL BE A FORTUNE TELLER. I'LL USE GRAN'S OLD CRYSTAL BALL.

HA-HA-HA! FREE OF MY PRISON AT LAST!

PRISON? IT WAS JUST THE LOFT, SILLY!

GRAN WARNED ME YOU WERE A BIT EVIL. IF YOU PROMISE TO BE GOOD, I'LL TAKE YOU TO THE GALA.

OR CAN YOU?! HA-HA-HA!

OKAY, I PROMISE! HA-HA-HA! YOU CAN TRUST ME!

I'LL TEST YOU OUT JUST TO MAKE SURE.

SO KORKY PUTS THE CRYSTAL BALL TO THE TEST...

READY?

YEP. WHAT'S THAT ON YOUR HEAD?

TEAS

FORTUNES TOLD

CLONG

IT'S A SHOWER CAP!

CAN YOU TELL MY FORTUNE?

YOU WILL MEET A...

DON'T TELL ME I'LL MEET A TALL, DARK STRANGER! THAT'S LAME.

...BOY IN A YELLOW AND RED JUMPER!

TWO WORDS.

BOR...

...ING!

YAWN

BERYL LEAVES AND...

FLUMP!

LET'S HAVE SOMETHING A LITTLE LESS RUBBISH NEXT TIME OR YOU'LL BE GOING BACK IN THE LOFT!

OKAY, OKAY!

SO...

I SEE SOMETHING FORMING IN THE MIST...

...YOUR HAT WILL GET YOU IN TROUBLE! HA-HA-HA!

EVERYONE AT THE BASE WEARS THESE!

THE CRYSTAL BALL WORKS ITS EVIL MAGIC...

THAT'S SILLY!

COLONEL GRUMBLY LOVES MY HAT!

POP!

HIS HAT?! IS THAT ALL YOU'VE GOT?!

I'M STILL WARMING UP.

AND...

IT'S BECOMING CLEAR...

...YOU'LL BE ATTACKED BY A RAPTOR! HA-HA-HA!

COOL!

YOU'RE TELLING CUTE LITTLE BABIES THEY'LL BE ATTACKED BY A RAPTOR?! YOU PROMISED TO BE GOOD!

THE CRYSTAL BALL WORKS ITS EVIL MAGIC AGAIN...

ARRRGH! RAPTOR!

GRRRRR!

BUT...

FASTER, HORSEY!

HUNT EMERSON

WHAT SORT OF RUBBISH CRYSTAL BALL ARE YOU?! HATS AND RAPTOR ATTACKS? IS THAT THE BEST YOU CAN DO?

HOW ABOUT A TIGER COMES TO HEAR ITS FORTUNE?

THAT WOULD NEVER...

...ARGGGH!

HA HA HA!!

GRRRR!

 # GREEDY PIGG

YUM! I'LL JUST TRY A NIBBLE.

AND...

URRGH! THIS ONE TIME I MAY HAVE EATEN TOO MUCH!

HA-HA-HA! LOOK AT JABBA THE GUTT!

HOW HAS HE GOT LIKE THIS?

FROM THE CRUMBS, IT LOOKS LIKE HE'S EATEN A GIANT CAKE!

THIS IS THE TRAIN THAT'S HEADING TO CACTUSVILLE FOR THE GALA. THE CAKE MUST HAVE BEEN FOR THAT!

THOSE POOR CACTUSVILLIANS!

WE CAN REPLACE THE CAKE WITH GREEDY'S SECRET CAKE STASH!

BUT IT'S SURROUNDED BY TOP SECURITY!

IT'S HARDER TO GET INTO THAN A THING THAT'S REALLY HARD TO GET INTO!

NO! DON'T! I NEED MY SECRET CAKE STASH IN CASE OF EMERGENCIES!

TIME TO LEAP INTO ACTION! GRUNT!

WIGGLE!

IN SCHOOL...

WHERE WILL WE FIND PIGGY'S SECRET CAKE STASH?

IT'LL BE REALLY HARD. HE WOULDN'T MAKE IT EASY FOR US!

OH. LOOK.

MR. PIGG'S SECRET CAKE STASH →

MEANWHILE...

I MUST COMMANDEER YOUR BICYCLE!

I'M ON THE MOVE NOW! I'M COMING TO SAVE YOU, MY GOODIES!

BACK TO SCHOOL...

THE CAKES!

THUNK! THUNK! THUNK! THUNK!

ARRRGH!

TRANQUILISER DARTS SET OFF BY FLOOR LASERS!

THERE'S ONLY ONE OF US LEFT NOW.

ZzzzZ

WHAT DO YOU MEAN? THERE'S TWO...

...OH.

ZZZ Z ZZZ

GOT TO BE EXTRA CAREFUL!

SUDDENLY...

ROLL!

MY CAKES!

ARRRGH!

THUNK! THUNK! ROLL!

Z Z Z Z

WAH! HE'S GAINING ON ME! I DON'T WANT TO END UP AS FLAT AS A PAN-CAKE!

JAM!

Z Z

DIVE!

SUCCESS! I'VE MADE IT! NOW TO GET THESE CAKES ON THE TRAIN.

CORPORAL CLOTT

FIDDLE O'DIDDLE

MULDOON IS MAKING A THING...

HO-HO! I'M SURE TO MAKE LOADS O' MONEY ON THIS HOOK-A-DUCK STALL I'M MAKING, SO I AM, TO BE SURE!

THE WEE KIDDIES WILL PAY TO HOOK THE LITTLE DUCKS IN THE HOPE O' GETTIN' THE ONE WITH THE STAR ON TO WIN THE STAR PRIZE...

...BUT THERE'S NO LITTLE STAR DUCKY! HO-HO-HO! TO BE SURE, SO THERE ISN'T!

I'LL HAVE A LITTLE PRACTICE, SO I WILL.

JUST AT THAT MOMENT FIDDLE O'DIDDLE APPEARS!

POP!

GASP!

WHERE'S THAT MULDOON?

HOOK!

HA-HA! I GOT YOU!

SO I HAVE!

I FINALLY GOT YOU! NOW YOU HAVE TO GRANT MY WISH, SO YOU DO!

ERM... BUT WHAT WISH? I'LL BE MAKING A TON O' MONEY ON HOOK-A-DUCK.

I COULD MAKE A TON MORE WITH ANOTHER STALL, SO I COULD!

MAKE ME THE BIGGEST FAIRGROUND ATTRACTION!

ZAP!

YOU GOT IT!

NOOO! NOT MAKE ME INTO THE BIGGEST ATTRACTION!

I DON'T WANT TO BE A BOUNCY CASTLE, SO I DON'T, TO BE SURE!

KEYHOLE KATE

USING HER MAGIC DOORKNOB, KATE ESCAPES THE ORDER OF NOSEY PARKERS...

WHERE AM I NOW?

N.A./CS.

AN OLD ABANDONED DOOR FACTORY! COOL! LOOK AT ALL THE KEYHOLES!

CAN YOU HANDLE IT?

OLD ABANDONED DOOR FACTORY

CLICKING HER HEELS IN KEYHOLE INFATUATED JOY!

HMMM, WITH ALL THOSE OLD DOORS, I COULD MAKE A THING FOR THAT 80TH GALA EVERYONE'S DOING STUFF FOR!

THAT WAS QUICK!

KATE'S MADE A DOOR MAZE! CAN YOU FIND YOUR WAY THROUGH? ONLY THE RED DOORS OPEN!

ANSWER:

YOU'RE RIGHT! I WONDER WHAT WILL HAPPEN IF I PULL THIS PIN?

PING!

CRUMP!

IT FALLS APART!

I'LL TRY AGAIN.

I'LL HELP YOU THIS TIME.

IT'S STARTING TO LOOK LIKE A ROBOT DRAGON!

WELL SPOTTED, DAD.

HAMMER! SPANNER! WRENCH! GRIP!

IT'S FUNNY – IF I **TRIED** TO MAKE A ROBOT DRAGON OR GORILLA, I WOULDN'T BE ABLE TO.

EVENTUALLY...

FINISHED!

WELL DONE. JUST ONE THING, BERYL...

...WE REMADE THE GORILLA! ARRRGH!

THUD!

THUD!

UD!

BRIGHTY

I'M SURE THEY'LL GET IT RIGHT EVENTUALLY! – ED

THE SMASHER!

SMASHER IS HAVING A KICK ABOUT...

OOPS!

NO! HOW WILL I FIX THAT BEFORE DAD SEES IT?

TOO LATE!

ARRGH! DAD!

LUCKILY FOR YOU I HAVE 36 SPARE SHEETS OF GLASS BECAUSE I KNOW EXACTLY WHAT YOU'RE LIKE!

A LETTER CAME FOR YOU. YOU CAN READ IT WHILE I SORT THIS OUT.

SLAM!

TOPPLE!

SMASH!

AN INVITATION TO MAKE SOMETHING FOR THE CACTUSVILLE GALA!

SMASHER BUILDS A COCONUT SHY...

HOW CAN I MAKE THIS MORE FUN?

SUDDENLY...

SOMEONE IS FLY TIPPING SOME OLD OFFICE EQUIPMENT IN THE MIDDLE OF THE STREET! RIGHT IN BROAD DAYLIGHT!

THAT'S BAD...

...BUT VERY GOOD FOR ME!

ROLL UP, ROLL UP! TRY MY SHY!

A COCONUT SHY? BORING!

NOT COCONUTS! DO YOU WORK IN AN OFFICE? EVER WANTED TO THROW YOUR STAPLER AT YOUR MONITOR?

HAVE I EVER?!

I WANT TO THROW A DESK FAN AT A PC TOWER!

ONLY A POUND A GO!

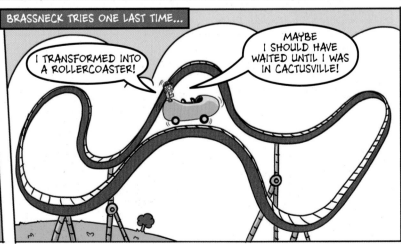

BLINKY GETS THE INVITE, TOO...
WHOOT!
THIS SAYS I'VE WON A MILLION POUNDS ON THE LOTTERY!
THAT'S NOT WHAT IT SAYS, BLINKY!

MEANWHILE, NEARBY...
G-G-GIMME ALL THE M-M-MONEY!
ER...
G-G-GIMME M-M-MONEY...

GASP! I'M SO NERVOUS! I CAN HARDLY SPEAK!
I'LL WRITE A NOTE.

I SHOULD STAND UP TO DAD... TELL HIM I DON'T WANT TO BE A BANK ROBBER LIKE HE WAS...
...I WANT A FLOWER SHOP!

LATER...
I NEED TO TAKE THIS TO LOTTERY HQ TO COLLECT MY MILLION!

BANK
HERE IT IS!
THAT'S NOT LOTTERY HQ, BLINKY - ED.

BUMP!
OOPS!
OOPS!

SORRY, MADAM.
MADAM?
YOU'VE PICKED UP THE ROBBER'S NOTE, BLINKY!

JUST THEN...
HERE WE ARE, BOYS!
POLICE
BANK

WHY ARE WE STOPPING HERE, SARGE? THIS ISN'T THE BEACH.
I'VE GOT NO MONEY. YOU WANT ICE CREAM, DON'T YOU?
THEY MUST BE ON A STAFF OUTING - ED.

INSIDE...
THERE WAS NO NEED FOR YOU ALL TO FOLLOW ME IN, LADS.
I NEED A WEE!

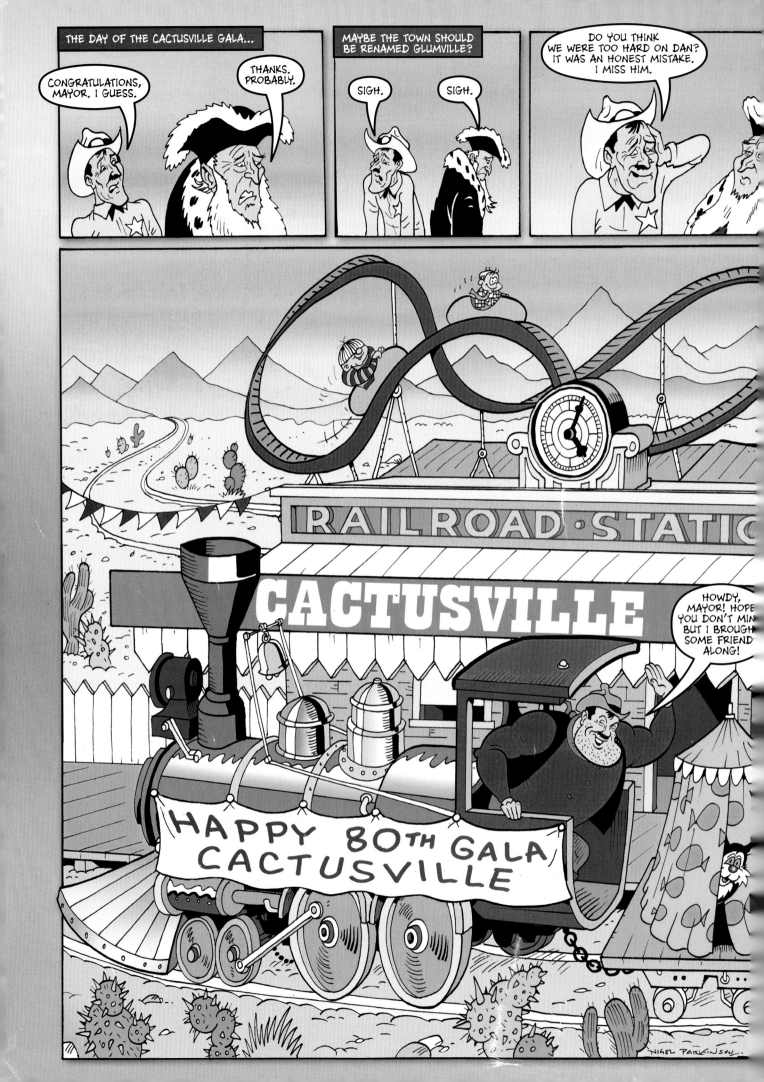